Turkey's Gift to the People

by Ani Rucki

SCHOLASTIC INC.

NEW YORK   TORONTO   LONDON   AUCKLAND   SYDNEY

For Stuart and Isabel Mace,
who taught me the importance of Turkey

Toklat near Ashcroft
Aspen, Colorado

ISBN 0-590-48122-3

12 11 10 9 8 7 6 5 4 3   4 5 6 7 8 9/9

Printed in the U.S.A.   14

First Scholastic printing, October 1994

NOTE: The illustrations in this book
were done using Berol Prismacolor® pencils.

Cover Design by David Jenney
Designed by Carolyn Gibbs

This story is based upon a traditional Navajo folktale. It is not meant to be an accurate retelling of the traditional folktale, but an adaptation and interpretation of it. "People" is used throughout the story in the Native American way of referring to animals as the Animal People, thereby acknowledging the close relationship between all forms of life.

Once there was a time when all the People of the world lived and worked together in perfect harmony. One day during this time, Crow was exploring far from home. It was a beautiful day. To the east, he saw the sun shining on the hills. To the south, he saw the wind blowing gently through the grasses. To the west, he saw the cool water dripping from the mountaintops to the streams below.

Crow headed north, flying farther and farther. Suddenly he saw something he had never seen before on the horizon. It was a great wall of water, taller than any tree and wider than any river, and it was headed right toward his people and his homeland.

Quickly, Crow turned and flew toward home, calling to the others along the way to warn them of the great wall of water that would soon flood their low, flat land.

The People gathered together and listened to Crow and they began to worry.

Bear said, "We must move to higher ground."

"But the mountains are too far away," said Butterfly.

"Then we must go to the hills," decided Bear.

The People agreed. "We must go to the hills and wait there for the water to recede."

When they finally reached the hilltops and looked toward the wall of water far off in the distance, the People discovered it was much larger than they had imagined. These hills were not high enough to protect them.

Then Mouse stepped forward. "I have an idea. These giant reeds are hollow, and their inside chambers are bigger than any cave. If we can get inside, we can wait there until the water passes."

Beaver knew this was her job. She began
to gnaw an opening at the base of the reed
so the People could get inside.

When Beaver finished, the People began to file
into the reed, two by two. But very quickly the
chamber became crowded, and the People realized
this single chamber could not hold them all.

"Beaver," said Moose, "climb onto my back
and chew a hole through to the chamber above."
So Beaver climbed onto Moose's back but she
could not reach the top of the chamber.

"Wait," said Spider. "I will weave a strong web for Beaver to climb so she can reach the top."

When Spider finished, Beaver climbed the web and chewed a hole through to the next chamber. In this way, Beaver and Spider worked together to open chamber after chamber, and the People followed them, moving farther and farther up the reed until everyone was inside.

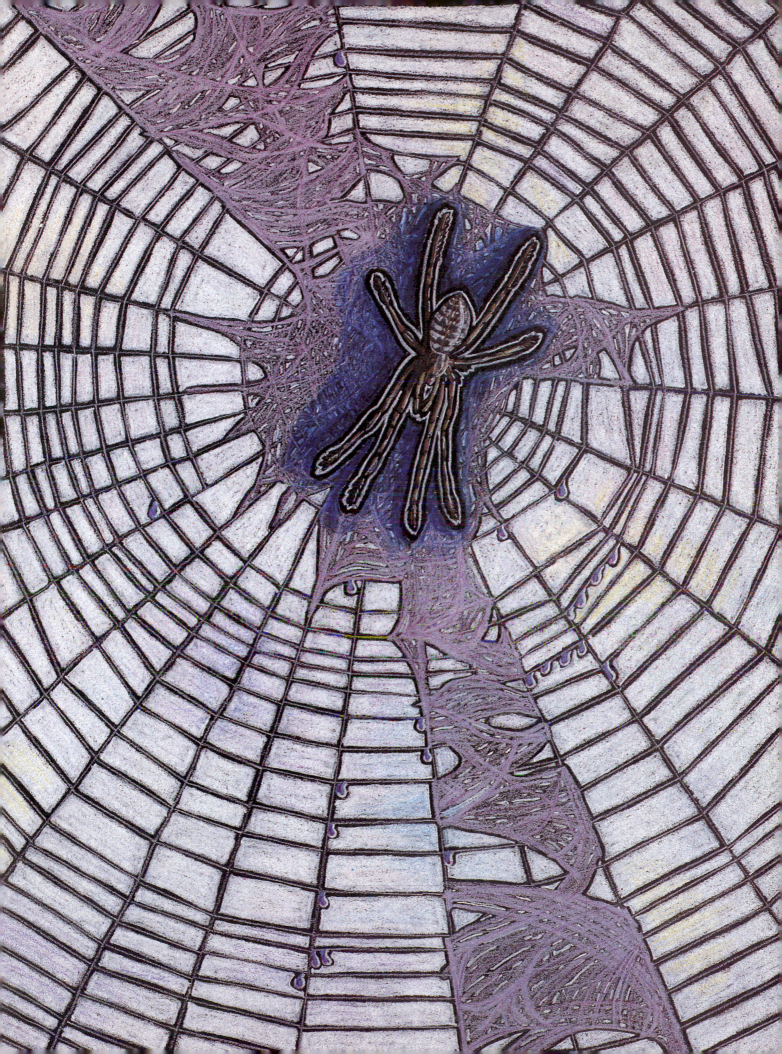

But Ground Squirrel was keeping track of everyone who entered the reed, and by his tally, one couple was missing. "Where are Mr. and Mrs. Turkey?" he shouted.

The People searched all the chambers of the giant reed, but the couple was nowhere to be found. Ground Squirrel stepped outside and looked anxiously toward the approaching wall of water.

Eagle knew he could help, so he swooped down out of the reed and circled high in the sky in search of his friends. Almost immediately he spotted them—running as fast as their short legs could carry them—just in front of the flood waters.

"Hurry!" Eagle shouted. "Come on! You can make it!"

It seemed like forever, but finally the couple flopped through the entrance to the reed, puffing and panting and gobbling. Everyone crowded around them, while Wasp quickly sealed the opening so no water could get inside.

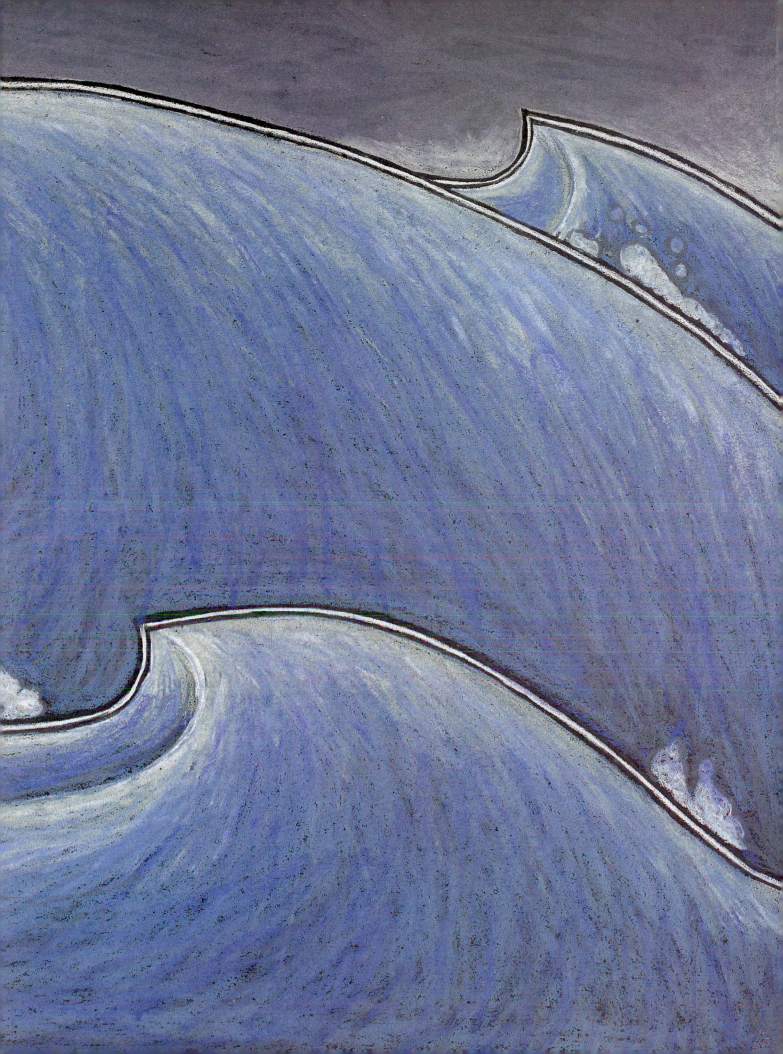

The People blurted out, "What happened? Where were you? You could have been killed!"

But Mr. and Mrs. Turkey were still trying to catch their breath. Finally, Mr. Turkey stood up and spoke.

"You forgot the seeds," he exclaimed.
Then he spread his feathers, letting the
thousands of seeds that he and his wife
had collected fall to the ground—the seeds
the People would need to rebuild and
survive after the flood waters receded.

All the People cheered. Each of them
had helped in his own way, but it was
Turkey who had remembered the seeds.

Ani Rucki is a fine artist and writer based
in Columbia, Maryland. A graduate of the
University of Maryland, Ms. Rucki was with
a publishing house in Boston before taking
time off to travel North America. She finds
mythology a valuable teaching tool, especially
for children, and retells this story because of
its cooperative lesson, unlikely hero, and
emphasis on the importance of seeds and
plants. This is her first published work.